First published by Parragon in 2012

Parragon
Queen Street House
4 Queen Street
Bath BA1 1HE, UK
www.parragon.com

Edited by Sarah Mellowes
Designed by Jonathan Ladd
Production by Jack Aylward

ISBN 978-1-4454-8621-5

Printed in Italy

# ANNUAL 2013

PaRragon

Bath · New York · Singapore · Hong Kong · Cologne · Delhi
Melbourne · Amsterdam · Johannesburg · Auckland · Shenzhen

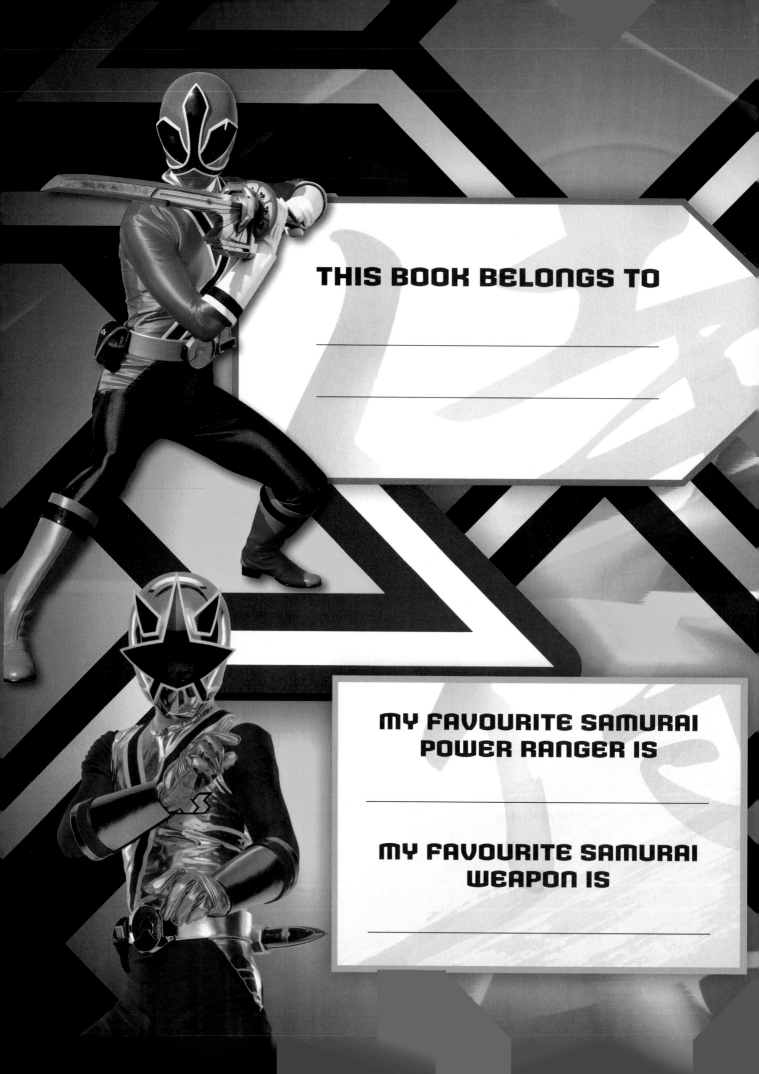

# THIS BOOK BELONGS TO

_____

_____

## MY FAVOURITE SAMURAI POWER RANGER IS

_____

## MY FAVOURITE SAMURAI WEAPON IS

_____

# CONTENTS

Ranger Profiles 8
My Ranger File 14
Samurai Outfit 15
What Would a Ranger Do? 16
Story: The Team Unites 18
Mentor Ji 26
Red Ranger Sketch 27
Go, Go Samurai! 28
Nighlok Shock! 29
Zord Zappin'! 30
Weapon-tastic! 32
My Own Zord 34
My Ultimate Weapon 35
Talk Like a Ranger 36
Story: I've Got a Spell on Blue 38
My Samurai Script 46
Mooger Colouring 48
Green Ranger Colouring 49
Super Samurai Game 50
Mentor Ji's Cypher 52
Shady Creatures! 53
Master Xandred Sketch 54
MegaMode Search 55
Cool Captions 56
Story: Jayden's Challenge 58
Welcome to the Netherworld 66
Meet the Nighlok 68
The Nastiest Nighlok 71
Would You Rather...? 72

Megazord Power 74
My Kanji Symbol 76
Maze in a Daze! 77
Story: The Blue and the Gold 78
Samurai Secrets 86
Megazord Colouring 88
Did You Know? 89
Ranger Party 90
Best Ranger Moments 92

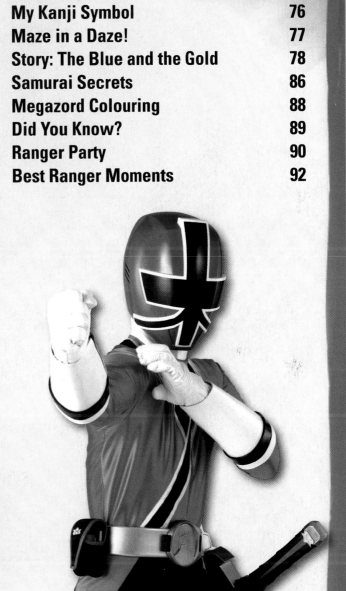

# Red Ranger

火 火 火

### Hey, I'm Jayden!

Jayden is the leader of the Power Rangers. He's been training with Mentor Ji since he was a young boy and puts his role as a Ranger before everything else – even his own safety! As he puts it, "One person is insignificant against saving the world."

Jayden tries to set the best example for the other Rangers. He's a deep thinker and doesn't say much, so when he does talk, everyone listens!

If Jayden ever doubts himself, he remembers the last words his father said to him...
"One day the great responsibility of being the Red Ranger will fall to you. Remember, protect the world from evil, stand by your allies and never run from a battle."

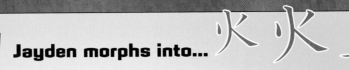

TOP SECRET

火 火 火

### Jayden morphs into...

### The Red Ranger!
The Red Ranger is the ultimate warrior and his fighting skills are mega! If a Nighlok gets too close, they can say hello to his Fire Smasher!

**Top quote:** "I need to be the best and keep getting better!"
**Element:** Fire
**Zord:** Lion
**Weapon:** Spin Sword / Fire Smasher
**Signature move:** Fire Smasher!

# Pink Ranger

### Hi guys, I'm Mia!

Mia is the confident big sister figure of the Power Rangers. She keeps an eye on the other Rangers and is the first one to notice if someone is feeling down.

Mia dreams of being a great cook, but really she's terrible! The other Rangers pretend they like her cooking so they won't hurt her feelings, but most of them would rather fight a Mooger than eat a piece of her cake – seriously, it's that bad!

**PINK RANGER**

## TOP SECRET

### Mia morphs into...

### The Pink Ranger!

Don't let the colour fool you – the Pink Ranger is one fierce monster fighter! She's been preparing for her role since she was a little girl. Anyone order a chopped Mooger sandwich?

**Top quote:** "Sky Fan! Hey, join my fan club. No autographs, please!"

**Element:** Sky

**Zord:** Turtle

**Weapon:** Spin Sword / Sky Fan

**Signature move:** Airway!

# Blue Ranger

水 水 水

### Hello, I'm Kevin!

Kevin eats, drinks and sleeps being a Samurai Ranger! He's Jayden's second-in-command, and aside from Jayden, he has the best technique of all the Rangers.

Kevin was a champion swimmer and left his dream of swimming in the Olympics to become a Ranger. His father trained him from birth, teaching him about discipline and how to become a master swordsman. Now, he spends every waking moment working on ways to improve himself – he's so dedicated to his training schedule that you could set your watch to the guy!

水 水

## TOP SECRET

水 水

### Kevin morphs into...

### The Blue Ranger!
The Blue Ranger believes his job is to fight evil with every breath in his body. In every fight, there's no doubt he's gonna bring it!

水

**Top quote:** "Every second I don't train is a second wasted!"
**Element:** Water
**Zord:** Dragon
**Weapon:** Spin Sword / Hydro Bow
**Signature move:** Dragon Splash!

# Yellow Ranger

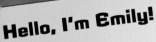

### Hello, I'm Emily!

Emily may be a sweet, innocent country girl, but she's also got the heart of a warrior. She was actually never supposed to be a Power Ranger – her sister was meant to be in the team, but an illness forced Emily to take her place. The other Rangers are very happy to have her and she trains hard to make her sister proud.

Everyone thinks Emily's the kindest of all the Rangers, and they love her fun attitude and ability to look on the bright side!

## TOP SECRET

### Emily morphs into...

### The Yellow Ranger

Super-sweet and super-fierce, the Yellow Ranger is no pushover!

**Top quote:** "Sticks and stones may break my bones, but words will never hurt me!"
**Element:** Earth
**Zord:** Ape
**Weapon:** Spin Sword / Earth Slicer
**Signature move:** Seismic Swing!

# Green Ranger

### Hey dudes, I'm Mike!

Mike is the funny, super-cool Ranger who can drive Kevin crazy because they're such opposites! Kevin thinks Mike needs to take his training more seriously, but Mike thinks Kevin could chill out a bit. Despite their differences, they're still great friends!

Mike doesn't mean to cause trouble, but he is a bit of a rebel! He loves video games and he can sometimes get distracted, but he's a very talented Ranger and knows how to be creative in a battle. He's 100% committed to being a Ranger... when he's not stopping for a bite to eat!

TOP SECRET

### Mike morphs into...

### The Green Ranger!
The Green Ranger has great Samurai instincts and more than one trick up his sleeve. He's also the king of the Nighlok insults!

**Top quote:** "Let's heat this up for this creepazoid!"
**Element:** Forest
**Zord:** Bear
**Weapon:** Spin Sword / Forest Spear
**Signature move:** Forest Vortex!

# Gold Ranger

### I'm Antonio Garcia!

The sixth Ranger to join the team is the fun Antonio! He and Jayden were best friends when they were young, but then Antonio had to move away. He promised Jayden he would keep training and find him again when Jayden became the Red Ranger. Jayden gave him the OctoZord as a leaving gift.

Antonio's the most outgoing and playful member of the group. Unlike the others, he hasn't had any formal Samurai training and mastered his fighting skills on his own. He's a technology whizz who uses electronic power symbols and even learned how to program his Zords!

GOLD RANGER

## TOP SECRET

### Antonio morphs into...

**The Gold Ranger!**
Blink and you'll miss him, because the Gold Ranger is super-fast! Being a Ranger is all he's ever wanted to do. Gold power!

**Top quote:** "When I promise some golden moments, I deliver!"
**Element:** Light
**Zords:** OctoZord and ClawZord
**Weapon:** Barracuda Blade
**Signature move:** Barracuda Bite!

光 光 光 光 光

# My Ranger File

Do you have what it takes to be the next Samurai Ranger? Could you take down a nasty Nighlok in one blazing strike? And could you be part of the fiercest fighting team ever? Fill in your Power Ranger profile and keep it safe!

My name is _____

My Power Ranger colour is _____

My best Ranger friend is _____

My top Ranger talent is _____

My cool catchphrase is _____

My ultimate weapon is _____

My best Ranger battle would be _____

_____

_____

Mentor Ji would like that I _____

_____

_____

_____

_____

Stick a photo of yourself here.

Draw your own Kanji Symbol here.

# Samurai Outfit

Get a photo of your face and stick it on the Ranger head. Now colour your Samurai outfit in your own awesome Samurai colours!

## Samurai ID

Cut out your personal Ranger card and carry it with you – you never know when those Moogers might turn up!

POWER RANGERS SAMURAI

..................................................

is an official Samurai Ranger.
Go, Go Samurai!

# What Would a Ranger Do?

To be a true Samurai Ranger, Mentor Ji says you must be brave, work as a team and not ever give up. Try this quiz to see if you would make decisions as well as Jayden and the gang!

**1**

Mentor Ji is making you practise the same old sword move for the millionth time, and you know you could do it with your eyes closed. Do you...

**A** Focus hard. The best Rangers always give 100%.

**B** Try to concentrate. It must be important if he's pushing you so hard.

**C** Ask if you can break for a snack – your stomach is growling like an angry Mooger!

**2**

You're about to leave the Shiba House to go to the cinema when the Gap Sensor sounds. Do you...

**A** Grab your Samuraizer and go – a Ranger is always ready.

**B** Groan that these stupid Nighlok have such bad timing, then go.

**C** Ask Mentor Ji if you can sit this one out – it is your favourite movie, after all!

**3**

You're fighting a Nighlok and he laughs and calls you a lame little Ranger. Do you...

**A** Tell him he's a slimy old creepazoid, then quintuple slash him with the other Rangers!

**B** Ignore his words, they don't mean anything. Use your Samurai sword to silence him!

**C** Get mad and upset – who does this wart-face think he is?!

**4**

A Nighlok has blasted and hurt your fellow Rangers, and now he's chasing after humans. Do you...

**A** Chase after the Nighlok – the safety of innocent humans always comes first.
**B** Help your Ranger friends – you can catch up with the Nighlok later.
**C** Take a rest. That fight really took it out of you!

**5**

Deker challenges you to a fight to find out who is the ultimate warrior. Do you...

**A** Tell him no, you only fight to protect others.
**B** Draw your sword. Of course you're the ultimate warrior, and you can prove it.
**C** Find the nearest large rock and hide – fast!

**6**

Master Xandred offers you a deal to make you the most powerful Ranger the Netherworld has ever seen. Do you...

**A** Tell him no chance. Is he a total birdbrain or what?!
**B** Tell him no – you'd like to be the most powerful Ranger, but you can't trust him.
**C** Say yes. Once you're the most powerful Ranger, you'll banish him!

## Find out if you're ready to join the Rangers!

### If you scored mostly As, you're...
### SAMURAI READY!

Wow, you really know your stuff! Get suited up, Ranger, because you're ready for battle. Go, Go Samurai!

### If you scored mostly Bs, you're a...
### SAMURAI TRAINEE

You may not have all the Ranger instincts just yet, but you're not far away. Remember, all of the other Rangers started out where you are.

### If you scored mostly Cs, you're a...
### RANGER ROOKIE

You'd better hit the training yard with Mentor Ji, because you've got a lot to learn before you can be let loose on a Nighlok. Practice makes perfect!

# The Team Unites

The Samurai Power Rangers were busy training at the Shiba House. As Mike watched Jayden and Kevin practising together, he felt as if he would never be able to use his senses as well as they could. Feeling sad, Mike crept off to see his old buddies down at the amusement arcade.

Meanwhile, deep in the Netherworld, in his ship on the Sanzu River, Master Xandred was busy putting Nighlok to work. Having only recently reawakened, he was not yet strong enough to travel into the human world himself, so instead he sent Nighlok monsters to unleash misery on the world.

"Let the tears of those crybaby humans fill the Sanzu River until it floods the world," he bellowed.

To help make this happen, he sent the giant-fisted Rofer through a gap into our world.

Back in our world, Mike was sitting with his old friends trying to make them see how he felt. But when he tried to explain about protecting the world from evil, his friends thought he was talking about a video game. Suddenly, there was a loud smash nearby and a giant fist came flying up through the pavement, followed by its owner, Rofer. Everybody ran away screaming, all except for Mike who leaped into action right away.

"I'll take care of this Nighlok on my own," he thought as he ran towards Rofer, pulling his Samuraizer from his pocket.

"Samuraizer! Go, Go Samurai!" he shouted as he ran along, using the magic tool to write the Forest Kanji Symbol that would morph him into the Green Samurai Ranger.

He did his best to fight Rofer, but the Nighlok's long arms could travel underground and come up for surprise attacks!

"I'm as cool as an iceberg, but I sting like a bee. It's tough to stop what you can't see!" gloated Rofer as his fist came smashing out of the ground, sending the Green Ranger flying through the air.

"If only I could use my senses as well as Jayden can," thought Mike. "There's no way I can defeat this Nighlok on my own."

Back at the Shiba House, the Samurai Rangers were alerted to Rofer's presence by the Gap Sensor and pinpointed the Nighlok's location on a special locator map. The rest of the team arrived to help the Green Ranger, but just as they did, the Nighlok began to dehydrate. When a Nighlok is away from the Sanzu River for too long, it starts to dry up.

"Uh-oh! Feels like I'm starting to dry out," said Rofer. "Guess I'd better punch out for now. Later, Rangers!"

And with that, he squirmed his way back into the Netherworld.

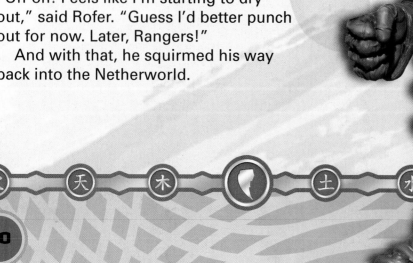

Back at the Shiba House again, Jayden spoke to Mike.

"You must stay away from your friends and family," Jayden explained. "It's the only way to protect them from evil."

Mike realized this was true and felt sad, but there was work to be done. He knew he had to find a way of sensing a Nighlok's attack before it comes, and he went away on his own to practise.

Meanwhile, back in the Netherworld, Rofer was bathing in the Sanzu River to recharge his powers.

"Now I'm gonna pound those Samurai Rangers into chopped liver!" said Rofer. "With the misery I'm gonna cause, soon this river will be fit to burst with human tears!"

When Rofer and the Moogers entered our world again, the Gap Sensor lit up. It didn't take long for the team to morph into the Samurai Rangers, but Mike still wanted to defeat Rofer by himself.

"We've got to help him," said Mia.

Grabbing their Spin Swords, the Samurai Rangers used their special powers against the Moogers, quickly defeating them, and leaving Rofer battling the Green Ranger.

"Bring it on, long arms," the Green Ranger yelled at his opponent.

Rofer didn't wait to be asked twice, and one of his fists was soon smashing its way underground towards the Green Ranger. Rofer was surprised when the Green Ranger started running away from him. The Green Ranger ran around and around, and Rofer's arm chased him wherever he went. Pretty soon, Rofer's arm was a tangled mess! But the Green Ranger had forgotten Rofer's other arm, which nearly caught him. Just in time, the Red Ranger arrived, stopping the second arm.

"Time to give you a taste of my Spin Sword," said the Green Ranger as he grabbed his weapon. "Spin Sword – Forest Vortex!" he yelled, using his special attack on the Nighlok.

With Rofer's arms still in a tangle, the Green Ranger soon defeated him.

The other Samurai Rangers congratulated the Green Ranger, but the battle wasn't over yet.

"Time for round two," said the Red Ranger. "He's coming back as a MegaMonster!"

The Green Ranger was still determined to defeat Rofer by himself. He grabbed his Samuraizer and FoldingZord so that he could go into MegaMode.

"Bear FoldingZord – MegaMode Power!" he shouted as he wrote the Kanji Symbol that means 'large' over the FoldingZord and morphed into MegaMode. With the Green Ranger at the helm of the BearZord, he battled Rofer while the others watched.

"We can't let him do this alone," said the Blue Ranger, and the other Samurai Rangers morphed into MegaMode as well.

"Rangers, we need to combine!" shouted the Red Ranger. "Zords, combine!" he commanded as he wrote the Kanji to combine the five Zords into the awesome Megazord.

"Samurai Megazord, we are united!" the Rangers all called out together.

Now they could fight Rofer as a team.

"Now, let's focus," said the Red Ranger. "If we work together we can use our instincts to sense Rofer's next move."

"What's the matter, did you fall asleep?" taunted Rofer. "Well, here comes your wake-up call!"

But as Rofer threw his mighty fist at the Megazord, the Rangers were ready for him. Anticipating his move, the Samurai Rangers soon had the MegaMonster all wrapped up. By working together they had won.

Back at the Shiba House, Jayden, Mia, Emily and Kevin all told Mike what a good job he'd done defeating Rofer.

"The way you got his arms all tangled up was so great," laughed Mia.

But Mike couldn't take all the credit.

"I only stopped one of his arms," Mike told the other Rangers. "It was Jayden who stopped the other arm. I couldn't have defeated Rofer on my own."

The Samurai Rangers all knew that the best way to work was as a team.

# Mentor Ji

## Welcome, Samurai Ranger. I am Mentor Ji.

Samurai must constantly improve their skills to ready themselves for battle.

Mentor Ji is the Rangers' teacher and shows them the way of the Samurai – patience, concentration and discipline. He's been a father figure to Jayden since Jayden was a child so they have a special bond, but he keeps a watchful eye over all of the Rangers.

## The Ranger Code
Mentor Ji teaches the Rangers to live by certain values. Sign your Ranger name next to these if you believe in them, too.

### Confidence
Power Rangers succeed because they believe in themselves and face challenges bravely.

_____ (sign here)

### Standing up for what's right
Power Rangers always look out for their friends, even if it means putting themselves second.

_____ (sign here)

### Health and fitness
Power Rangers stay one step ahead of fish-face Moogers by keeping fit and training hard.

_____ (sign here)

### Teamwork
Power Rangers succeed in missions by working together as a team.

_____ (sign here)

### Friendship
Power Rangers are the best of friends, and they support each other, no matter what.

_____ (sign here)

# Red Ranger Sketch

Look closely at the small picture of the Red Ranger and then use the gridlines as a guide to copy him into the larger grid. When you're finished, colour him in. Good luck, Ranger!

# Go, Go Samurai!

A good Samurai must have an eagle eye if they want to be one step ahead of the enemy. Can you spot six differences between these pictures of the Rangers? Tick a lightning strike for each one you find.

Answers:

# Nighlok Shock!

Uh-oh! An evil Nighlok has jumbled up all the answers to these questions! Can you find the correct answers by unscrambling the words? Pair up each word with a question by writing a number in each circle to show your answer.

1) What is the Blue Ranger's real name?

2) What is Master Xandred's noodle-faced sidekick called?

3) Who is Dayu still in love with?

4) What mega weapon does the Red Ranger use?

5) What is the name of the special house where the Rangers live?

6) What is the river of human tears in the Netherworld called?

7) Finish this saying: Rangers together, Samurai _____!

8) What is it about the Nighlok Yamiror that stinks so badly it could knock you out?

VINEK ○
___ ___ ___ ___ ___

ZUSAN ○
___ ___ ___ ___ ___

BTHREA ○
___ ___ ___ ___ ___ ___

RIFE SHERAMS ○
___ ___ ___ ___  ___ ___ ___ ___ ___ ___ ___

FREEVOR ○
___ ___ ___ ___ ___ ___ ___

KREED ○
___ ___ ___ ___ ___

ROOCOOT ○
___ ___ ___ ___ ___ ___ ___

ASHBI ○
___ ___ ___ ___ ___

# Zord Zappin'!

The Samurai Rangers' Zords are like pets! Jayden's little Lion FoldingZord will hop into his hand to play, but when he calls it for battle it grows into a fierce attack vehicle. Check out the special animal Zords below.

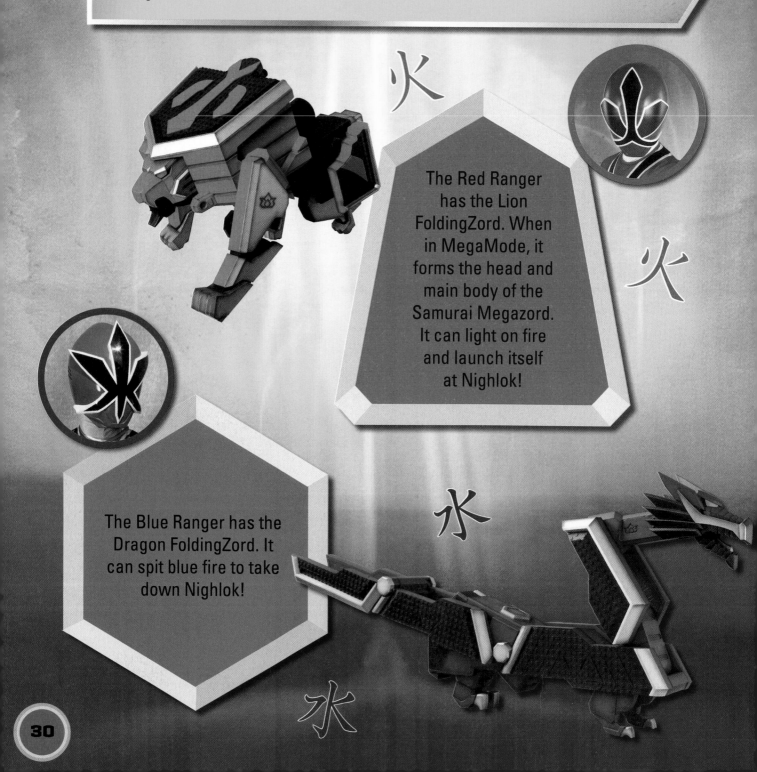

The Red Ranger has the Lion FoldingZord. When in MegaMode, it forms the head and main body of the Samurai Megazord. It can light on fire and launch itself at Nighlok!

The Blue Ranger has the Dragon FoldingZord. It can spit blue fire to take down Nighlok!

The Gold Ranger has the OctoZord and the ClawZord. The OctoZord can fly and spit black ink that blinds the enemy. When in MegaMode, the Claw Battlezord has four different battle modes!

The Green Ranger has the Bear FoldingZord. It rears up on its hind legs to tackle bad guys!

The Pink Ranger has the Turtle FoldingZord. When in MegaMode, it can use the power of the wind to create a tornado!

The Yellow Ranger has the Ape FoldingZord. It can strike the evil Nighlok with its fists.

# Weapon-tastic!

Each Ranger has their own Spin Sword that can become a Mega Blade to pilot their Zord. But they also all have their own special weapon, connected to their unique element.

**Samurai Ranger, Fire!**

**Samurai Ranger, Water!**

**Samurai Ranger, Sky!**

The Blue Ranger has the **Hydro Bow**, which shoots bursts of laser arrows. This bow and arrow packs a real punch!

The Red Ranger has the giant **Fire Smasher**! Powered by his Lion Disc, it can also be upgraded to a fireball-shooting cannon when the other Rangers add their Power Discs.

The Pink Ranger has the **Sky Fan**. When she attaches her Turtle Disc, she can control the wind, blowing Nighlok back to the Netherworld!

Samurai Ranger, Forest!

The Green Ranger has the powerful **Forest Spear**, which can create super-strong leaf storms! Have no fear with the spear!

Samurai Ranger, Light!

The Gold Ranger has the **Barracuda Blade**, which he uses in his high-speed slash attacks. His final strike is the Barracude Bite!

Samurai Ranger, Earth!

The Yellow Ranger has the **Earth Slicer**. When combined with the Ape Disc, she can fling it like an explosive boomerang!

# My Own Zord

Have you thought about what your Zord would be like? Choose wisely, because these little creatures are your battle partners!

Pick your favourite animal from this list (or choose your own).

Eagle ☐

Crocodile ☐

Tarantula ☐

Stingray ☐

My Zord is a _____.

What special powers does your Zord have?

_____

Which word best describes your pet Zord in its small form? Tick your favourite.

Draw your Zord here. Don't forget to match the colours to your own Ranger suit!

Loyal ☐

Cheeky ☐

Funny ☐

Playful ☐

Which word best describes your Zord in battle mode? Tick your favourite.

Fast ☐

Powerful ☐

Strong ☐

Intelligent ☐

# My Ultimate Weapon

Have you decided what your Mooger-mashing weapon would be? Fill in the details below to help you form the most awesome Ranger weapon ever!

Pick your favourite weapon from this list (or choose your own).

**Dagger** ☐

**Laser Gun** ☐

**Club** ☐

**Boomerang Blade** ☐

**Poisoned Darts** ☐

**Hammer** ☐

My ultimate weapon is a _____

What is its Ranger-tastic name? _____

How does it defeat Nighlok? _____

Draw your ultimate weapon here.

# Talk Like a Ranger

You might have noticed that the Rangers don't miss a beat when it comes to Nighlok backchat. The nasty Nighlok have some mean one-liners, but a smart Ranger can fight insult for insult!

**What the Rangers say when they're getting ready for a fight...**

- Ready to roll!
- Let's heat this up!
- Let's do this thing!
- I'll give it all I've got!
- We gotta take these Nighlok down!

**What the Rangers say after a good battle...**

- I got some new moves to go with my Samurai groove!
- Fantastical!
- Excellente!
- That was unreal!

**Best Ranger comebacks ever...**

- Let's take it to this slimeball!
- Moogers to the left of me, Moogers to the right, but when I get done with them, they all say goodnight!
- With all the teeth I'm knocking out, I hope they have a good dental plan!
- Oh man, the Moogers! It's a whole school of fish faces!
- What's wrong with you? Didn't anyone ever hug you as a kid?
- Fighting Moogers is easy – like chopping down weeds back home!

## How would you answer these nasty Nighlok zingers?

"Hey, did you fall asleep? Well, here comes your wake-up call!"

"Humans are a waste of good space!"

"You're a blade of grass and guess who's going to be the lawnmower?"

"You attack like a toothless gator – useless!"

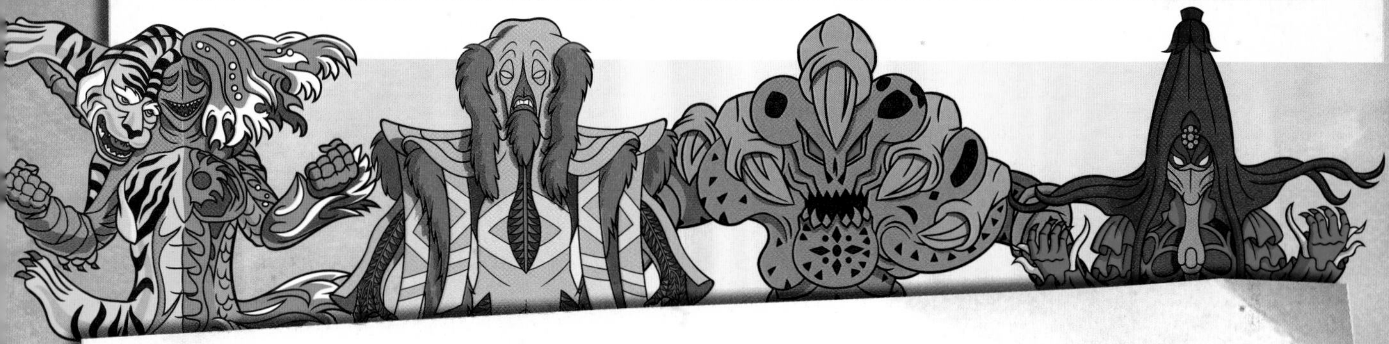

"I've seen glaciers that move faster than you!"

"You're cruisin' to a losin'!"

"Such a nice day...let's change that!"

"The forecast calls for rain...my rain of pain!"

# I've Got a Spell on Blue

Kevin was practising his sword skills with Jayden one morning at the Shiba House.

"Wow! Kevin's technique is really good," said Mia.

"They're both so good, I hate to think what would happen if they had to fight each other," added Mike.

"That would NEVER happen," said Emily.

水　火

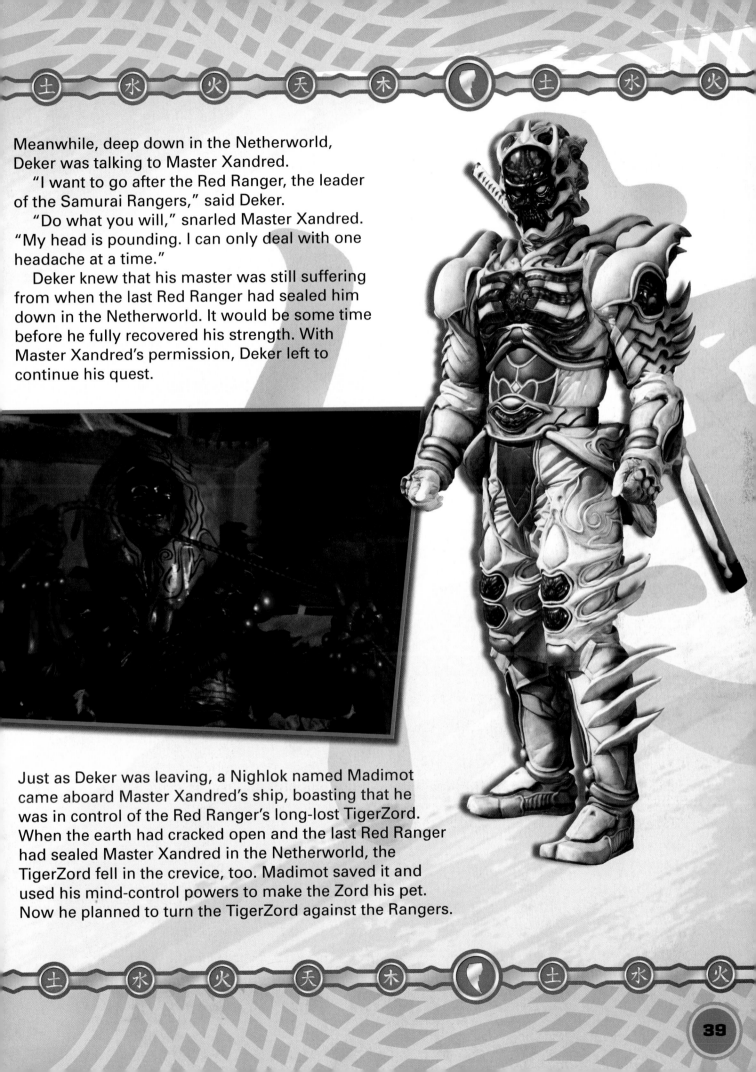

Meanwhile, deep down in the Netherworld, Deker was talking to Master Xandred.

"I want to go after the Red Ranger, the leader of the Samurai Rangers," said Deker.

"Do what you will," snarled Master Xandred. "My head is pounding. I can only deal with one headache at a time."

Deker knew that his master was still suffering from when the last Red Ranger had sealed him down in the Netherworld. It would be some time before he fully recovered his strength. With Master Xandred's permission, Deker left to continue his quest.

Just as Deker was leaving, a Nighlok named Madimot came aboard Master Xandred's ship, boasting that he was in control of the Red Ranger's long-lost TigerZord. When the earth had cracked open and the last Red Ranger had sealed Master Xandred in the Netherworld, the TigerZord fell in the crevice, too. Madimot saved it and used his mind-control powers to make the Zord his pet. Now he planned to turn the TigerZord against the Rangers.

As Madimot entered our world, the Gap Sensor at the Shiba House lit up to alert the Samurai Rangers.

In a flash, the Rangers were ready to confront him, but were amazed to see that he had the powerful TigerZord under his power.

The Rangers knew they must get the TigerZord back, but Madimot shot out a mind-controlling ray at the Rangers.

"Everyone duck!" yelled the Red Ranger.

But the Green Ranger was too slow and the ray was coming right at him. Bravely, the Blue Ranger pushed the Green Ranger out of the way and the ray hit him instead.

The Blue Ranger was now under Madimot's evil control and started to fight his fellow Rangers. Madimot sent a mind-control blast towards the Red Ranger, who countered the ray with his special Resist Disc.

Although the Rangers fought well, Madimot had both the Blue Ranger and the TigerZord on his side, and managed to overpower the Green, Yellow and Pink Rangers. The Red Ranger had no choice but to use his powers to transport the others to safety, leaving the Blue Ranger and the TigerZord with Madimot. But Madimot was drying out and needed to get back to the Sanzu River for a soak that would recharge his powers.

"You wait here until I get back," he said as he ordered the Blue Ranger to stay with the TigerZord.

While Madimot was busy in the Netherworld, Deker was in our world. Being only half Nighlok, he was not so interested in harming humans – instead his wish was to fight the ultimate duel. Fighting the Red Ranger would fulfil that desire, and Deker needed to keep tabs on his future opponent, for one day they would meet in battle.

火

水

Meanwhile, Madimot couldn't resist having some fun with the Blue Ranger, who was still in his power. Together, they were causing mayhem at a local construction site. Not wanting to endanger his fellow Rangers, Jayden set off to face Madimot and the Blue Ranger alone. When Mia, Mike and Emily realized this, they followed him, knowing that it was their duty to help.

Meanwhile, Jayden was facing an impossible choice – if he didn't fight the Blue Ranger, Madimot would order the Blue Ranger to turn his sword on himself. Shortly after the other Rangers arrived, Jayden morphed into the Red Ranger and began his unwilling battle with the Blue Ranger.

水

As the Rangers watched the fight, they were unaware that a nearby stranger was Deker in human form. After watching the Red Ranger fight, Deker was more certain than ever that the Red Ranger was the right opponent for the ultimate duel.

As the Red Ranger fought, he tried to get close enough to the Blue Ranger to use the Resist Disc to break Madimot's spell. Attaching it to his Spin Sword, he freed him from the Nighlok's control.

Now that all the Rangers were a team again, they morphed and sprang into action to help battle Madimot.

"You guys take care of the Nighlok. I'll handle the TigerZord," said the Red Ranger.

While the others raced off to battle Madimot, the Red Ranger prepared to face the TigerZord.

"LionZord! MegaMode Power!" he yelled as he wrote the magic Kanji Symbol that would call up his Zord.

As soon as he was in the cockpit, the TigerZord charged at the LionZord with its claws spinning. This was tougher than the Red Ranger had thought, but as soon as he was able to knock down the TigerZord, the Red Ranger leaped into the Zord and placed the Resist Disc in the control panel.

"TigerZord! Resist Power!" he yelled, and Madimot's power was lifted once again.

The TigerZord was back where it belonged. With the whole team against him, Madimot was soon defeated – but every Nighlok has a second life as a MegaMonster!

The Red Ranger and the TigerZord began battling Madimot while the other Rangers went into MegaMode, ready to help him. After they all morphed into MegaMode, the Red Ranger wrote the magic Kanji Symbol for 'combination' and the five Zords combined to form the massive Megazord.

"Samurai Megazord! We are united!" shouted the Rangers together.

"Samurai Artillery!" yelled the Red Ranger, and the TigerZord combined with the Megazord.

"Tiger Drill Megazord! Armed for battle!" shouted all the Rangers together in the Megazord cockpit.

The Tiger Drill Megazord and Madimot battled fiercely. Even Madimot's powerful shield was no match for the Tiger Drill, and before long Madimot was defeated for good.

"Samurai Rangers, victory is ours!" said the Red Ranger triumphantly.

Another battle against a Nighlok had been won, but the Red Ranger knew there would be more to come. A Samurai Ranger is always on guard!

# My Samurai Script

Now you can talk like a Ranger, it's time to write your very own Ranger battle scene! Fill in the blanks below to show what the characters are saying, then act out the scene with your friends. You'll need eight people, or you can play more than one part.

## LIGHTS, CAMERA, ACTION!

**Mentor Ji:** That's the Gap Sensor. I can see on the Locator Map that there's a Nighlok at City Hall!

**Red Ranger:** Come on, Rangers. Let's go.

**Green Ranger:** I can't wait to crush those fish-face Moogers!

**Gold Ranger:** This is gonna be gold!

**Mentor Ji:** Be careful, Rangers. Work together and don't give up.

**All Rangers:** We will, Mentor Ji.

The Rangers arrive at City Hall.

**Nighlok:** Well, if it isn't the Samurai Power Lamers!

**Red Ranger:** _____

**Blue Ranger:** _____

**Nighlok:** I could crush you with all six hands tied behind my back!

**Pink Ranger:** _____

**Yellow Ranger:** _____

The Rangers take out their Samuraizers.

**All Rangers:** Samuraizers! Go, Go Samurai!

The Rangers get suited up.

**All Rangers:** Samurai Rangers, ready!

**Nighlok:** Get ready for six fistfuls of pain, Lamers!
**Gold Ranger:** _____

All of the Rangers battle the Nighlok and eventually defeat him!

**Red Ranger:** This isn't over yet, Rangers. He's coming back as a MegaMonster. Time for MegaMode!
**Nighlok:** That's right. Back for a dose of delightful despair?
**Red Ranger:** Lion FoldingZord!
**Pink Ranger:** Turtle FoldingZord!
**Blue Ranger:** Dragon FoldingZord!
**Green Ranger:** Bear FoldingZord!
**Yellow Ranger:** Ape FoldingZord!
**Gold Ranger:** Octo FoldingZord — I need you!
**All Rangers:** MegaMode Power!

The Rangers form the Megazord and fight the Nighlok.

**Nighlok:** How can it be? The Lamers are beating me?!
**Green Ranger:** _____
**All Rangers:** _____
**Red Ranger:** _____

The Rangers all celebrate their victory!

# Mooger Colouring

Watch out, Rangers!
The monstrous
Moogers are ready
to attack!

# Green Ranger Colouring

The Green Ranger launches a powerful spear attack!

# Super Samurai Game

The Rangers have found new power from a special Black Box and have now become the Super Samurai Rangers! Master Xandred has unleashed an extra-nasty Nighlok who is taking toys from children to steal their tears! Take your place as one of the Super Samurai Rangers and make your way through the board – whoever gets to the end first has defeated the Nighlok! But watch out for dangerous traps along the way....

**START**

**1**

**2**

**3**
You tasted Mia's cooking! Move back 1 space.

**6**
You made it to training on time. Move forward 2 spaces.

**5**

**4**

**7**

**8**

**9**
A Mooger just got past you. Move back 2 spaces.

## HOW TO PLAY

- Find up to six Ranger-ready players.
- Get a dice.
- Cut out your Ranger counters.
- Each player chooses a Ranger counter and places it on the START box. Whoever rolls the highest number goes first.

**For 2–6 players**

**Dice required**

## GO, GO SAMURAI!

**FINISH**

**24**
Bad attitude, Ranger. Move back 5 spaces.

**23**

**22**

**18**
You listened to Mentor Ji. Roll the dice again.

**19**

**20**

**21**

**17**
Great Nighlok insult! Move forward 3 spaces.

**16**

**15**

**14**
Your weapon just failed. Move back 3 spaces.

**10**
You protected a fellow Ranger. Move forward 5 spaces.

**11**

**12**

**13**
You tried to go it alone. Miss a turn.

# Mentor Ji's Cypher

Mentor Ji has a training challenge for you, Ranger. He has a special message that he's coded with numbers. Can you work it out to reveal and understand his message?

12    26 5 25 22 21 1    8 3 21 15    14 12 21    18 3 21 15 19 16

12    17 3 25 16,    13 6 5    3 5    14 12 21    12 19 26 22

6 23 25 22 22 5    12    5 25 16 16

| 1 | 2 | 3 | 4 | 5 | 6 | 7 | 8 | 9 | 10 | 11 | 12 | 13 |
|---|---|---|---|---|---|---|---|---|----|----|----|----|
| G | H | I | J | T | U | V | W | X | Y  | Z  | A  | B  |

| 14 | 15 | 16 | 17 | 18 | 19 | 20 | 21 | 22 | 23 | 24 | 25 | 26 |
|----|----|----|----|----|----|----|----|----|----|----|----|----|
| C  | D  | E  | F  | K  | L  | M  | N  | O  | P  | Q  | R  | S  |

_ _____ ____ ___ _____

_ ____, ___ __ ___ ____

_____ _ ____.

# Shady Creatures!

The creepy monsters of the Netherworld are lurking in the shadows, ready to jump out on unsuspecting humans! Can you spot who is who to help the Rangers find them?

# Master Xandred Sketch

Look closely at the small picture of Master Xandred, if you dare!
Then use the gridlines as a guide to copy him into the larger grid.
When you're finished, colour him in! Be careful, Ranger!

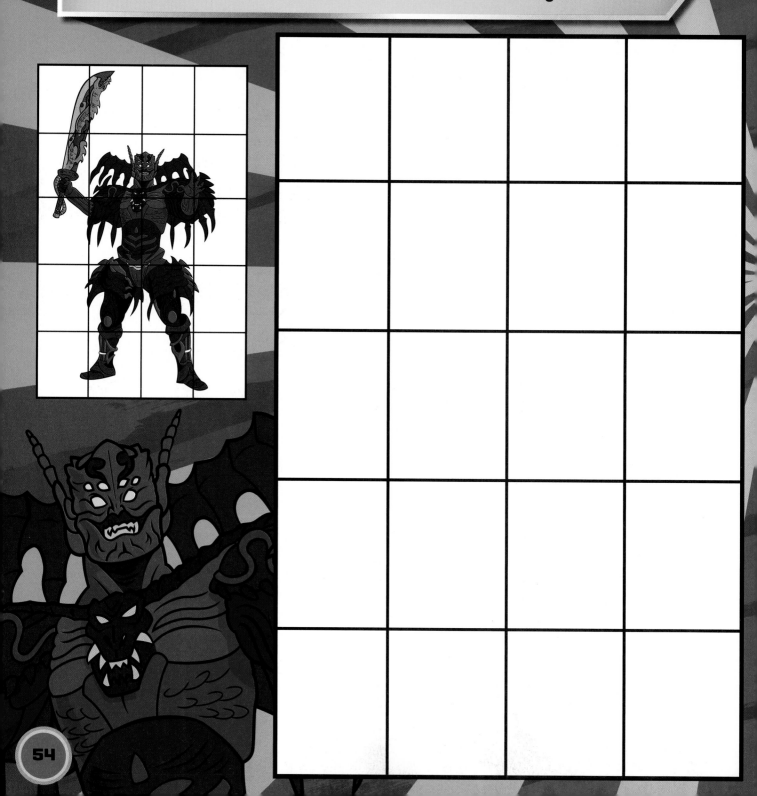

# MegaMode Search

Focus on your Samurai skills of observation! Can you find these smashing Samurai words in the grid? Look forwards, backwards, up, down and diagonally.

```
N S L G Q V I H M D Q E
S E H N Y E R Y I N Y L
K A D I N C K D K T L F
M U M Y B I T R E M I F
E J N U A A N O A U M M
N L S V R J J B S G E S
T M I L Y A M O M G C K
O L U N N I I W A H M Y
R M E I A P Q Z P B M F
J I V R I K O L E I N A
I E P E K R C S V R U N
K R X C D O I N O T N A
```

JAYDEN

KEVIN

MEGAZORD

MIKE

EMILY

ANTONIO

MENTOR JI

SHIBA

HYDRO BOW

MIA

SKY FAN

SAMURAIZER

55

# Cool Captions

Do you know what's happening in these pictures? Fill in the bubbles to show what the Samurai Rangers are talking about. You could use your imagination and try out some jokes!

# Jayden's Challenge

Jayden, the Red Ranger, is the only Ranger with the power to seal Master Xandred and the Nighlok back in the Netherworld. Master Xandred and the Nighlok monsters were getting stronger by the day. The Samurai Rangers would have lost their last battle with Robtish if it hadn't been for the half-human Nighlok, Deker, stepping in to save the Red Ranger. He wanted to save the Red Ranger for himself, believing it was his destiny to battle Jayden in the ultimate duel. The Samurai Rangers had been wounded in their last battle and Jayden didn't want to put them in any more danger. He felt he must defeat the Nighlok alone.

When Master Xandred discovered how Deker had saved the Red Ranger, he was furious and went with his Moogers to destroy Deker. But Deker, who was more powerful than Master Xandred had realized, managed to get away.

"This is far from over!" roared Master Xandred as Deker made his escape.

Robtish was still angry with Deker, too. He decided to squirm his way through a gap back into our world to have another go at defeating the Red Ranger.

Meanwhile, Jayden was by himself walking around the city. He watched some children playing in the park.

"This is the way life should be," he thought to himself. "Happy and carefree, with no monsters to worry about."

All of a sudden, Robtish appeared with a horde of Moogers.

"Run away, kids!" yelled Jayden, as he prepared to fight.

Back at the Shiba House, the other Rangers were worried about Jayden.

"Jayden doesn't want to put you in any more danger," explained Mentor Ji to the other Rangers. "This is something he wants to do alone."

However, when the Gap Sensor went off, they wanted to go and help Jayden.

"We're in this together," said Mia. "We can't let Jayden do this by himself."

The other Rangers agreed and they raced off to help.

When they arrived on the scene, the Rangers told Jayden they were in this together.

"Somebody's got to stop the Nighlok," Jayden told his friends, "and I'm glad it's us!"

"Rangers together! Samurai forever!" chanted the team as they morphed into Samurai Rangers, ready to fight.

Working as a team, the Rangers soon defeated the Moogers before facing off against Robtish. Now the battle was between Robtish and the Samurai Rangers. Using his Samurai senses, the Red Ranger was able to predict Robtish's next move. He warned the Rangers to be ready for Robtish to send out a shock wave. While the Rangers deflected the wave, Jayden was getting ready with a trick of his own.

"Say hello to my Fire Smasher!" the Red Ranger shouted.

"Five Disc Tiger Cannon – Rangers, lend me your discs!" he called to the others.

With their combined powers, the Samurai Rangers overcame Robtish. However, within seconds, Robtish came back to fight some more, this time as a MegaMonster.

"Lion FoldingZord! Turtle FoldingZord! Dragon FoldingZord! Bear FoldingZord! Ape FoldingZord!" cried out each of the Rangers in turn. "MegaMode Power!" they all shouted together.

In MegaMode, the Rangers were very powerful, but they were never stronger than when they worked as a team.

"Zords, combine!" they commanded in unison.

The five Zords locked together to form the awesome Megazord. Now the Samurai Rangers felt ready for anything. But the Rangers hadn't bargained on the MegaMonster's next trick – flying Moogers!

"Perhaps the Samurai Battlewing could help?" suggested the Green Ranger.

But the Blue Ranger had another idea.

"What if we combine the Samurai Battlewing with the Megazord?" he said.

This was an idea that the Blue Ranger had been working on for a while, and he had some diagrams to show how it could work.

"First, we must combine the TigerZord, the BeetleZord and the SwordfishZord to create the Samurai Battlewing," said the Blue Ranger as he sprang into action.

The Samurai Battlewing blasted one shot at Robtish to distract him while it split into pieces and attached itself to the Megazord.

It was now a Battlewing Megazord that Robtish and his flying Moogers had to face.

Now that the Megazord could fly, it wasn't long before the flying Moogers were wiped out.

"Bye, bye, birdies!" laughed the Yellow Ranger.

It was just Robtish that the Rangers had to battle.

"Looks like we saved the worst for last," said the Red Ranger, as they prepared to fight.

Robtish was very powerful, but the Rangers launched an aerial attack on him.

"Let's fly up so we can take him down," said the Blue Ranger.

The Samurai Rangers activated their Mega Blades and from way up in the air they dived down on the MegaMonster. With one great slash of their mighty blade, Robtish was finally defeated.

"Samurai Rangers, victory is ours!" said the Red Ranger proudly.
 The Red Ranger knew there was still a lot of work left to do before the Nighlok were defeated, but he was very glad he had his team there to help him do it.

# Welcome to the Netherworld

The Netherworld is a dark world where strange, evil creatures called Nighlok live. The Nighlok can't go far from the Sanzu River that runs through the Netherworld without drying out, but they can sneak in through gaps for short times to cause mayhem!

The Nighlok's evil plan is to get enough human tears to cause the Sanzu River to overflow – then it will spill over into the real world and they will escape forever! Unless the Rangers can stop them, of course....

Now, wanna see what scary looks like?

### Master Xandred

Master Xandred is the leader of the Nighlok monsters and the most evil creature you're ever likely to come across! He recently reawakened after being shattered into a million pieces years ago by Jayden's father, the last Red Ranger. To say he has a bone to pick with the Rangers is an understatement! He's not yet strong enough to travel to our world so he sends other Nighlok to do his dirty work....

MASTER XANDRED

## Octoroo

Ooh-aah-ooh, I'm Octoroo! Master Xandred's noodle-faced sidekick calls himself 'the brains behind Master Xandred', but that's not saying much! He's a short, octopus-like creature who advises Master Xandred about the secrets of the Netherworld and the Rangers, and suggests the best ways to challenge the heroes! This is one slippery character.

## Dayu

Half human, half Nighlok, Dayu has survived in the Netherworld only because Master Xandred likes her music. But Dayu has a dark secret: centuries ago she was tricked by one of Master Xandred's Nighlok into trading her human life to save her one true love...Deker! The only item she was allowed to take from the human world was her precious guitar. Although the guitar has now transformed into the ugly 'Harmonium', Dayu still loves it above all else.

## Deker

Even though he is half Nighlok, Deker has no interest in hurting humans. Instead, he's cursed with the desire to fight the ultimate duel and won't find peace until that happens. After seeing the Red Ranger in battle, he knows he has finally found a worthy opponent! Unfortunately for Dayu, Deker remembers nothing from his past as a human with her.

**Turn over to meet some of Master Xandred's nastiest Nighlok!**

# Meet the Nighlok

## DATA FILE: ROFER

This ugly dude's mega long arms can punch through solid ground and concrete, and attack his victims from underground! Watch out, or he'll serve you a knuckle sandwich!

## DATA FILE: DOUBLETONE

Doubletone is a sneaky monster who tricks victims into giving up on their dreams. It's no surprise the Rangers aren't his biggest fan!

## DATA FILE: DREADHEAD

It's a hairy situation with Dreadhead! A super-strong Nighlok, he's immune to most of the Power Rangers' weapons and is only defeated after they master the powerful Beetle Disc.

## DATA FILE: NEGATRON

According to this nasty Nighlok, "If the truth hurts...excellent!" Negatron taps into the minds of his victims and gives insults that turn their emotional pain into physical pain. Ouch!

## DATA FILE: YAMIROR

Ew, what is that stink?! Yamiror is a monster with the stinkiest breath you've ever smelled! It's so bad that it knocks the Rangers out of action!

## DATA FILE: MADIMOT

I put a spell on Blue.... Madimot has the power of mind control, and it's so strong that the Blue Ranger falls under his spell and fights the other Rangers!

## DATA FILE: DESPERAINO

Can you weather this storm? This monster can conjure up downpours with raindrops that bring despair to everyone they fall upon! The forecast is for sad showers....

## DATA FILE: VULPES

Vulpes spies with his inter-dimensional mirror, trying to discover Jayden's secret Power Symbol. But it's not long before the Red Ranger gives him seven years' bad luck!

## DATA FILE: STEELETO

This strong Nighlok thinks scaring humans is child's play! He can use the blades on his body to attack his victims. Luckily, the Rangers are able to cut in!

## DATA FILE: SPLITFACE

A particularly scary Nighlok, Splitface steals the spirits of his victims. He can break his body into lots of parts, making it very difficult to fight him. For the Rangers, it's like dodgeball with teeth!

## DATA FILE: ARACHNITOR

Spider-features Arachnitor plots with Octoroo to take over Master Xandred's throne by trying to discover the Red Ranger's Sealing Power Symbol. Watch out, or he'll leave you in a sticky situation!

## DATA FILE: SCORPIONIC

Summoned by Master Xandred to scare the humans, Scorpionic is the first Nighlok to almost defeat the Red Ranger in battle. Of course, the Red Ranger won. Choke on that, Scorpionic!

# The Nastiest Nighlok

None of Master Xandred's Nighlok have managed to defeat the Power Rangers yet, but that won't stop him from trying! If you were fighting one of these evil creatures, what do you think he would look like?

My worst enemy Nighlok would be called
_____

Draw your nasty Nighlok here! The Rangers had better watch out for this guy!

His special powers are _____
_____

His evil weapons are _____

His catchphrase is _____

He makes humans cry by _____

He would try to beat me and the Rangers by
_____

His biggest weakness is _____
_____

Pick some words to describe what he looks like. Tick as many as you like.

**HAMMER FISTS** ☐   **HAIRY** ☐

**TWO HEADS** ☐   **SLIMY** ☐

**SHARP TEETH** ☐   **TENTACLES** ☐

**HORNS** ☐   **WHEELS FOR FEET** ☐

**TALL AND SKINNY** ☐   **SPOTTY** ☐

# Would You Rather...?

If you were a Samurai Ranger, and you had to choose, which of these funny situations would you pick? Try these out yourself and then test your Ranger friends, too!

**Would you rather...**

Eat one of Mia's awful cakes

**OR**

Have to stick to Kevin's crazy training schedule for a week?

**Would you rather...**

Go on a fun fishing day with Antonio

**OR**

Go play awesome video games with Mike?

**Would you rather...**

Mentor Ji caught you playing games when you were supposed to be training

**OR**

Let a Mooger get past you in a battle?

**Would you rather...**

Fight a terrifying duel with Deker

**OR**

Stay overnight in the Netherworld...alone?

**Would you rather...**

Be a whizz with technology, like the Gold Ranger

 OR

Be a great acrobat, like the Yellow Ranger?

**Would you rather...**

Have the responsibility of being the leader, like Jayden

 OR

Be a bit of a cool rebel, like Mike?

**Would you rather...**

Have a shot of the Red Ranger's Fire Smasher

 OR

Ride in the cockpit of the Megazord?

**Would you rather...**

Swim in the Sanzu River

 OR

Get totally slimed by the Nighlok, Antberry?

**Would you rather...**

Stay with Spike and Bulk for a week

 OR

Stay in the Shiba House for a day?

**Would you rather...**

Become the next Red Ranger

 OR

Help the Rangers defeat Master Xandred once and for all?

# Megazord Power

## Samurai Megazord, We Are United!

When the Power Rangers need to defeat a MegaMonster Nighlok, they go into MegaMode. The Zords they control grow extra large, and they can combine them to create super warrior robots!

The Samurai Megazord is a combination of the original five Zords – Ape, Turtle, Dragon, Lion and Bear – but the Rangers can add on other Zords to create even more weird and wonderful battle vehicles. Everyone ready for a costume change?!

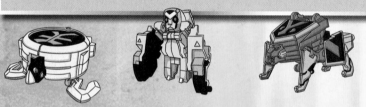

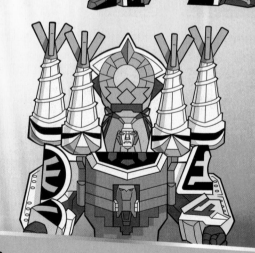

### Samurai Megazord + BeetleZord = Beetle Blaster Megazord

Created by combining the BeetleZord and the Samurai Megazord. When Dreadhead transforms into a MegaMonster Nighlok, the Samurai Rangers form the Beetle Blaster Megazord to defeat Dreadhead for good!

### Samurai Megazord + TigerZord = Tiger Drill Megazord

Created by combining the TigerZord and the Samurai Megazord. Jayden figures out how to break Madimot's mind-controlling spell and forms the Tiger Drill Megazord to destroy the Nighlok!

## Samurai Megazord + SwordfishZord = Swordfish Fencer Megazord

Created by combining the SwordfishZord and the Samurai Megazord. When Kevin returns with the special Zord, it unleashes a healing rain and the Rangers regain their strength, forming the Swordfish Fencer Megazord to defeat the Nighlok!

## TigerZord + BeetleZord + SwordfishZord = Samurai Battlewing

This aerial Megazord is formed when the TigerZord, BeetleZord and SwordfishZord combine. It is piloted by the Red, Green and Blue Rangers. With the help of the Samurai Megazord, the Battlewing defeats MegaMonster Desperaino!

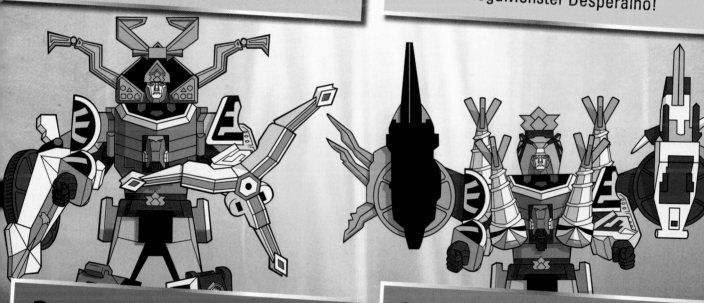

## Samurai Megazord + Gold Ranger's OctoZord = Octo Spear Megazord

This impressive Megazord is formed by combining the Samurai Megazord and the Gold Ranger's OctoZord. During a battle with the MegaMonster Steeleto, Antonio combines these two Zords to form the Octo Spear Megazord, freezing Steeleto with icy breath and destroying him!

## Samurai Megazord + Samurai Battlewing = Battlewing Megazord

This amazing Megazord is formed when the Samurai Megazord and Samurai Battlewing combine. When flying Moogers were too much for the Samurai Megazord, the Rangers combined the Samurai Battlewing and Samurai Megazord to help them defeat the giant Robtish!

# My Kanji Symbol

The Power Rangers' Kanji Symbols all represent their special element and control their powers.

Which Ranger's Kanji Symbol would you choose? Once you've decided, try drawing it in the box below. Like Mike, it might take a bit of practice! When you're ready, you'll be able to draw it in the air, like the Rangers do with their Samuraizers!

The Red Ranger's symbol means **FIRE**.

The Pink Ranger's symbol means **SKY**.

The Blue Ranger's symbol means **WATER**.

The Green Ranger's symbol means **FOREST**.

The Yellow Ranger's symbol means **EARTH**.

**Draw your symbol here!**

# Maze in a Daze!

The Pink Ranger has been caught in Rhinosnorus's dreamworld. The Blue Ranger must find her before Rhinosnorus wolfs her down, never to wake up again! Can you help him through the maze as fast as you can?

# The Blue and the Gold

At the Shiba House, Antonio, the Gold Ranger, was showing the other Rangers the ClawZord. Mentor Ji had hidden away the battle-damaged Zord for years.

"Mentor asked me to perform a bit of my tech-whizz magic," said Antonio, pleased to have an important task to do.

As the Rangers stared at him, fascinated by the new Zord, Antonio reached for his Samuraizer and pressed a button to make Samurai symbols appear.

Antonio thought that showing the Rangers his hi-tech skills could help prove him to be a worthy Samurai Ranger. However, Kevin thought differently – Antonio was showing he was a computer nerd, not a Samurai.

"I know I wasn't born into the Samurai life like you guys, but I'm trying to help in my own way," Antonio said, realizing how difficult it would be to convince Kevin.

Later, Mike, Mia and Emily spoke to Antonio, and Antonio explained that he felt he had already proved himself in battle.

"Eat, drink, sleep being a Samurai. It's the only way to impress him," said Mike, knowingly.

From now on, Antonio knew it was his mission to prove himself to Kevin.

Down in the dark Netherworld, Dayu was telling Master Xandred that Octoroo was working on a big scheme, and if it worked, all Nighlok would be able to escape the Sanzu River for good.

"Huh! Good!" snarled Master Xandred. "If that squid brain can really pull it off, then putting up with that lame blabbermouth all these years will be worth it!"

Back in our world, Octoroo was looking down a dark well, deep inside a forest.

"Kiddies' eyes will be crying and Nighlok will have a place to get wet when they're drying!" Octoroo cackled.

The Nighlok Antberry then set out to steal children's toys, followed by a horde of Moogers.

光
光 光

At the Shiba House, Antonio was working on his plan to prove himself to Kevin. He planted tiny cameras around the house in order to spy on Kevin's every move. At the stroke of midnight, when Kevin finally tucked himself into bed, Antonio went to bed, too.

Meanwhile, the Nighlok Antberry was using his sneaky skills to steal every child's toy in sight. Antberry targeted Bulk and Spike, stealing Spike's favourite teddy bear mascot. The next morning, Bulk and Spike could see a trail of slime where the teddy bear once sat!

At the Shiba House the next day, Antonio was spying on Kevin as he prepared to go for a run.

"Training and more training. Everything precisely timed," Antonio said quietly to himself.

Antonio decided to follow him into the forest. Suddenly, an evil chuckle rang out through the trees, stopping Kevin in his tracks.

"Did you hear that, Antonio?" asked Kevin, a little way ahead of Antonio.

Antonio couldn't believe Kevin knew he'd been spying on him!

"So, why the spy cams?" Kevin asked, frustrated.

"I just wanted to see what a true Samurai does," replied Antonio.

Kevin explained that being a Samurai was the real deal – it wasn't like being in a spy movie. However, he knew that right now they had to work together to find out where the evil laugh was coming from.

Deep in the forest, Octoroo was looking at all of the toys Antberry had managed to steal from children.

"It's brilliant! By tossing exactly 30 beloved toys in the well, the sorrow it causes will make the river rise and fill the well once again!" said Octoroo, quickly instructing Antberry to get to work chopping up the toys.

Before the well dried up a while ago, it was the Nighlok's main portal into the real world. Octoroo needed to get it working once again!

Kevin and Antonio were watching their every move. Kevin tried to get hold of Jayden, but the signals were blocked. Suddenly, Octoroo struck the rock with a fiery blast and Kevin and Antonio quickly morphed into the Blue and Gold Rangers. Octoroo had put up secret barriers, which had jammed their phone signals, so they were unable to get help.

"Time to enjoy my new toy! Sanzu slime!" shouted Antberry, as he blasted a sheet of slime over the Rangers.

"Hey! My blade's as slippery as an eel!" cried the Gold Ranger, unable to keep hold of his Barracuda Blade.

The Blue and Gold Rangers left their weapons behind and started to fight Antberry with their Samurai moves. But Antberry was too slippery for them to get a grip on!

Octoroo joined in by blasting them into the air. Then he unleashed the Moogers on them.

"Alright, Moogers, go finish those pests off!" Octoroo ordered.

While the other Rangers were at the Shiba House worrying about their friends, Kevin still couldn't get a signal on his phone. With Antonio's arm now injured, he decided to fight the Nighlok alone. However, within minutes, Kevin was cornered by Moogers.

"Back off, Moogers!" shouted Antonio, coming to Kevin's rescue.

Antonio managed to take down the Moogers, but Kevin was annoyed that he had stepped in and put himself at risk.

"Being a Samurai is more than just following ancient traditions," Antonio said. "It's about being a warrior, a protector of all things good."

Kevin realized Antonio was right, and he had the true spirit of a Samurai. He told Antonio the other Rangers would turn up soon, as he wasn't at the house in time for practice.

As Kevin and Antonio reached the top of a slope, a wall of Moogers stood waiting.

"Take a deep breath, 'cause the battle's about to begin," said Antonio.

They quickly morphed into the Blue and Gold Rangers and went head-to-head, defeating the Moogers in seconds. Just as Antberry was about to chop up the first toy, the Rangers attacked him from above, and the evil axe fell into the well.

"Even if you can hold your weapons, you can't slip away from me!" cried Antberry, knocking both Rangers to the ground.

Suddenly, a huge fire-strike sent Octoroo and Antberry flying. The other Samurai Rangers had come to the rescue!

The Red Ranger's blazing strike overpowered Antberry's sheet of slime, and quickly turned him into a fiery blaze. The Rangers' amazing Samurai moves then finished him off, sending him into the dark well.

Within moments, Antberry turned into a MegaMonster, ready to fight!

"MegaMode Power!" the Rangers shouted in unison.

The Rangers jumped into their Zord cockpits, joined by the Gold Ranger with his special OctoZord.

"Octo Spear Megazord! Armed for battle!" the Rangers cried.

The Megazord wasn't able to get a grip on the slimy Antberry, so they blasted out ice to freeze him. Then they used their electric spear to take him down for good!

When they returned to the Shiba House, all they had left to do was give back the stolen toys to the children.

"We get to make things right. That's the great thing about being a Samurai, right Antonio?" said Kevin.

Antonio had proven himself to be a great Ranger in battle, and Kevin had finally accepted him into their Samurai team.

# Samurai Secrets

Jayden has the responsibility of being the Red Ranger, which means there are some important things that he just can't share with the other Rangers. We found out that his father was the one who sealed Master Xandred to the Netherworld and that Jayden is the only Ranger with the Sealing Power, but does Jayden have more secrets?

What are your biggest secrets? Write them here, then use a glue stick lightly on the edge of the pages and fold them in half. Stick them together gently and if anybody else is flicking through your book, they'll skip right by them! Only you will know where they are!

I would secretly love to _____

I really don't like _____
_____
_____
_____

I always _____
_____
_____
_____
_____
_____

I really like ______________________________
______________________________________________
______________________________________________

I never ______________________
______________________________
______________________________
______________________________

I think about ______________________________
____________________________________________

I have always wanted to ______________________________
______________________________________________________
______________________________________________________

Top secret 1 ______________________________ TOP SECRET

Top secret 2 ______________________________ TOP SECRET

Top secret 3 ______________________________ TOP SECRET

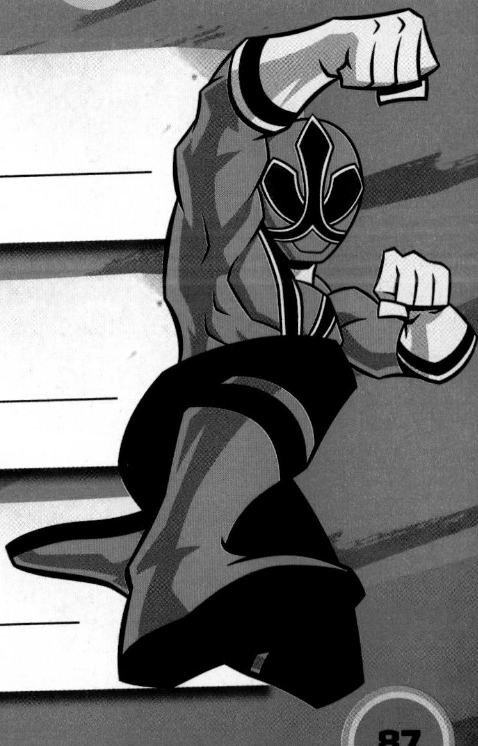

# Megazord Colouring

The Beetle Megazord strikes a MegaMonster Nighlok!

# Did You Know?

Are you the most mega Ranger fan ever?! Check out these Samurai Ranger facts and see how many you already know!

Mia, the Pink Ranger, used to sing.

Spike has a huge crush on the Pink Ranger and is always dreaming about her.

Jayden promised the young Antonio that he would one day make him a Samurai.

Not only were Deker and Dayu married, it was him that gave her the guitar that became her beloved harmonium!

Emily can play the flute.

Jayden and Antonio met at the fish market where Antonio's father worked.

When Jayden gave Antonio the OctoZord when they were young, Mentor Ji was angry and told him to get it back. Jayden said he would quit being a Samurai before asking for it back!

Mike can skateboard!

Mentor Ji says that Jayden is one of the best at swordfighting that has ever been!

Despite training for years to be a Ranger, Kevin was the last to receive his amulet – from his father when he got the call-up to be a Ranger.

Spike's most treasured possession is a large stuffed panda he won at the amusement park, called Sammy!

# Ranger Party

Would you like to treat your friends to the ultimate Ranger day? Here are some quick tips to make your party Samurai Ranger ready!

## Ranger Invite

✂

You're invited to

_____'s

Samurai Power Rangers party

at _____ on

_____

The Shiba House address is

_____

_____

### Rangers together, Samurai forever!

Make copies of this Samurai Ranger invite and fill one in for yourself. Then hand out the other copies to your Ranger guests.

## Decorations

Decorate your house to look like the Shiba House. Draw a Gap Sensor alarm for the wall and place a map on the table as your Locator Map. Set aside a training area and a meeting area with comfy seats. You could be Mentor Ji!

## Food

Rangers are all about power food to build up their energy for battle!

• Serve homemade milkshakes for your Ranger guests. Milk helps to build strong bones. A glass a day keeps the Moogers away!

• Make up a big fruit platter with all your favourite and most colourful fruits. Fruit can help your body heal and it keeps teeth and gums strong!

• Finally, take a leaf out of Mike's book and go for pizza! It's his favourite and it's what all of the Rangers eat when they're chilling out.

## Games

### Master Xandred's Ranger Detector

Gather your Ranger players into a circle. One player is chosen to be Master Xandred, on the hunt for Samurai Rangers! Master Xandred is blindfolded and stands in the middle of the circle. Everyone in the circle should march round in a clockwise direction until Master Xandred points his hand and shouts, "Who gives me this headache?" The person he is pointing at is the chosen Ranger! They have to say "Rangers together, Samurai forever!" back to Master Xandred, but the trick is to disguise their voice so Master Xandred can't guess who they are! If Master Xandred guesses correctly, the chosen Ranger becomes Master Xandred – if not, the game continues!

### Mentor Ji's Mirror

If you can read an enemy's moves then you're one step ahead of them! Players stand facing a friend. Decide who is going to lead – the other person tries to copy the leader exactly. The leader should start slowly, then gradually get faster to test the other player's skills!

### Rangers Ready

Gather your party friends together to watch a Power Rangers episode. Every time one of these things happens, you have to perform the action:

• Mentor Ji speaks ➡ You say "Yes, Mentor Ji."

• You hear "Samurai Ranger, ready!" ➡ Write your Kanji Symbol in the air with your hand.

• Someone mentions the Sanzu River ➡ Take a gulp of your juice.

• Every time you see a Nighlok ➡ Shout "Samurai Strike!"

• When you first see a Megazord ➡ Everyone do a group huddle in the middle of the room and shout, "We are united!"

# Best Ranger Moments

What Samurai Ranger moments do you remember the most? Was it the episode where the Rangers entered the dreamworld and Bulk thought he was a hero? Or was it that amazing time the Rangers first saw the Gold Ranger fighting in battle? Fill in your top memories here!

My favourite Ranger is _____

I loved it most when he/she _____

_____

_____

_____

My favourite line he/she's ever said is _____

_____

_____

My favourite episode is _____

The best Nighlok ever is _____
_____
_____

The funniest thing that's happened is _____
_____
_____

The scariest moment was when _____
_____
_____

The ultimate battle was _____
_____
_____